MEGA PUZZLES

PIRATES

bookoli

Connect the dots to reveal a creature lurking in the deep.

Answer on page 46

Land ahoy! Guide the ship safely through the storm and to the island.

Start

Finish

Answer on page 46

A pirate never forgets! Test your memory by looking at this picture for one minute. Cover it up and answer the questions.

Can you remember...

1. How many treasure chests there are? ....

2. What is on the pirate flag? ....

3. What animal is lurking in the cave? ....

4. How many pirate hats there are? ....

Answers on page 46

So many swords! How many can you count here?

I can count ☐ swords.

Answer on page 46

Pirates love counting up their silver! Can you complete all of the sums below?

(1) 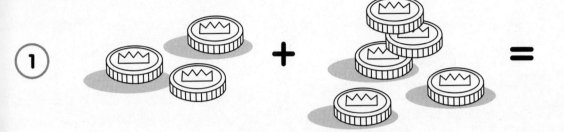 + =

(2)  + =

(3) + =

(4)  + =

Answers on page 46

Thar, she blows! How many cannon balls can you count in the scene?

I can spot ⬜ cannon balls.

Answer on page 46

Join the dots to complete the pirate flag and get ready to set sail!

Answer on page 46

Help this pirate reach the island by hopping on stepping-stones with even numbers: 2, 4 and 6. Quick, before the tide comes in!

Start

Finish

Answer on page 46

Adventure ahoy! Can you spot six differences between the pictures of this secret island?

Answers on page 46

Follow the directions to find out where the treasure is buried.

1. **North 6 squares**
2. **East 4 squares**
3. **South 2 squares**
4. **West 1 square**
5. **North 5 squares**
6. **East 3 squares**

Start

Now draw an X to mark the spot!

Answer on page 46

This captain is counting up his plunder. Work out the missing numbers in each tower of gold by adding together the numbers in the two bars below it.

a

1 2 2

b

2 3 3

c

4 2 3

Answers on page 46

Imagine you are about to set off on a voyage! Draw all the places you will visit on your map.

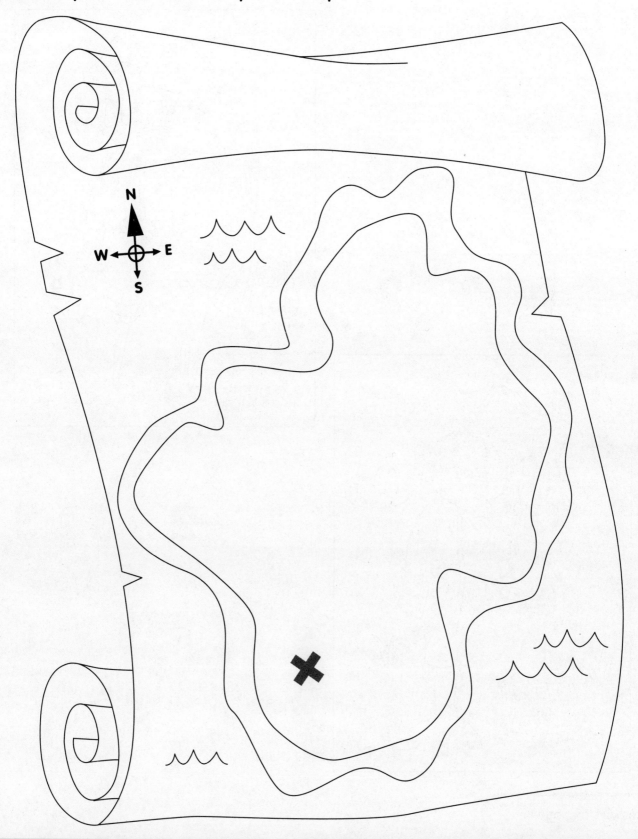

Double trouble! Can you spot six differences between these pictures of the terrible pirate twins?

Answers on page 46

This pirate is pulling his fiercest face! Can you spot him in the crowd?

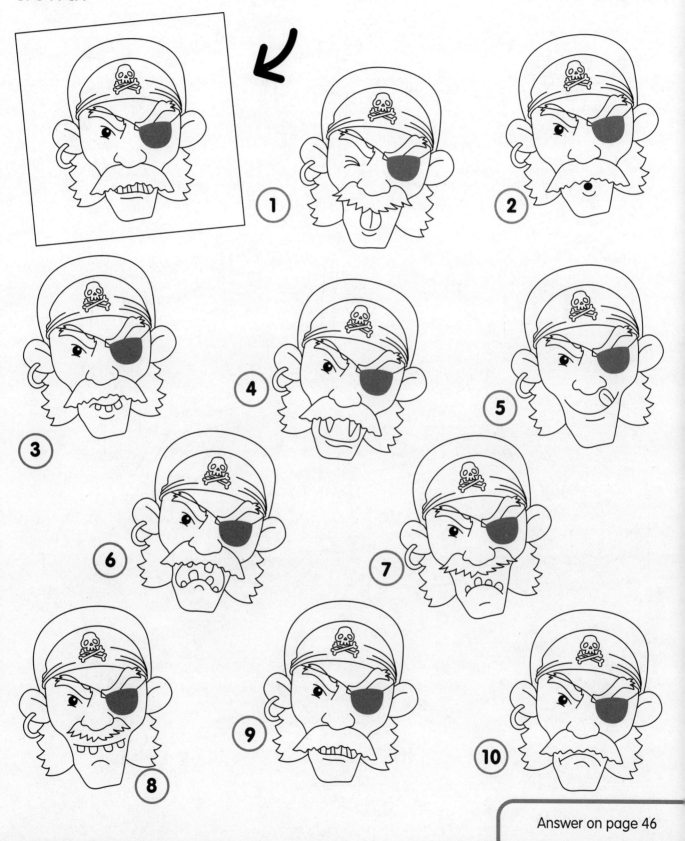

Answer on page 46

Squawk! Follow the wiggly lines to match each pirate to his pet parrot.

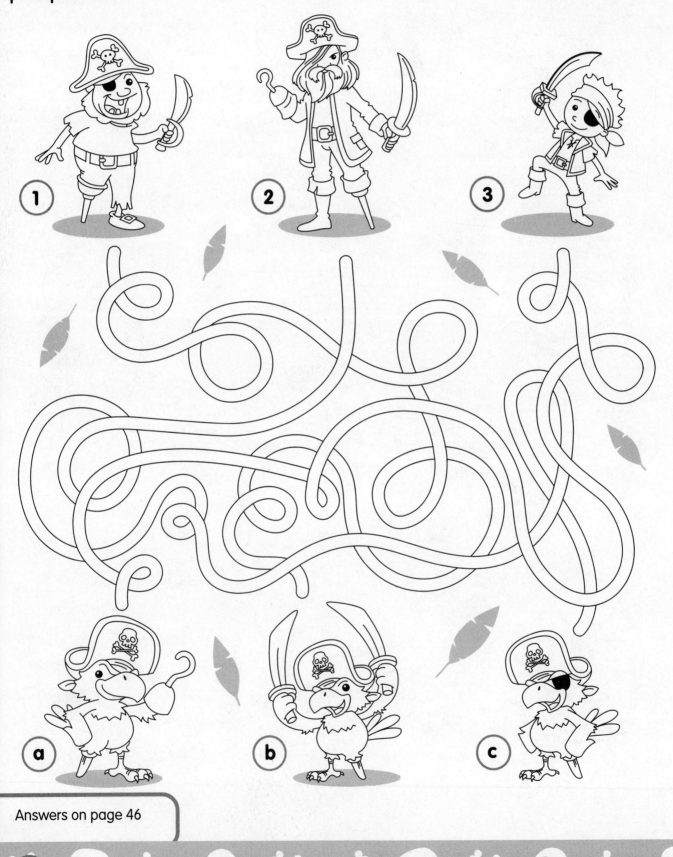

Answers on page 46

Draw in the missing jewel in each row.

1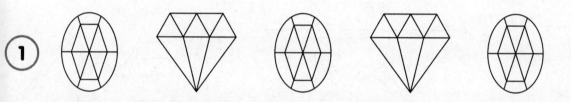

2

3

4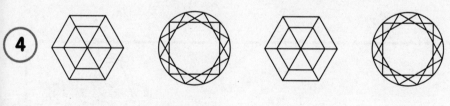

5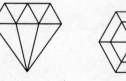

Answers on page 46

Search the ship for the five objects from the panel.

It's a perfect night to sail under the stars. Can you spot five differences between the pictures?

Answers on page 46

This pirate wants to join a crew, but a crew can only have 7 pirates. Count the pirates in each group to see which one she should join.

a

b

Answer on page 47

It's shipwreck sudoku! Draw in the missing objects. Remember, each item can only appear once in each row and column.

Answers on page 47

This fearless captain is searching for the legendary sea monster. Follow the directions to find the beasty.

Start

1. North 6 squares
2. West 1 square
3. North 3 squares
4. East 7 squares
5. South 1 square

Answer on page 47

Cross out the pirates that appear twice to reveal the famous Captain Crabby, master of the high seas.

Answer on page 47

How many of each object can you spot on the busy beach?

It's time for some sea shanties! Can you spot six differences between the pictures of this crooning crew?

Answers on page 47

Can you spot Captain Redbeard amongst these pirate impostors?

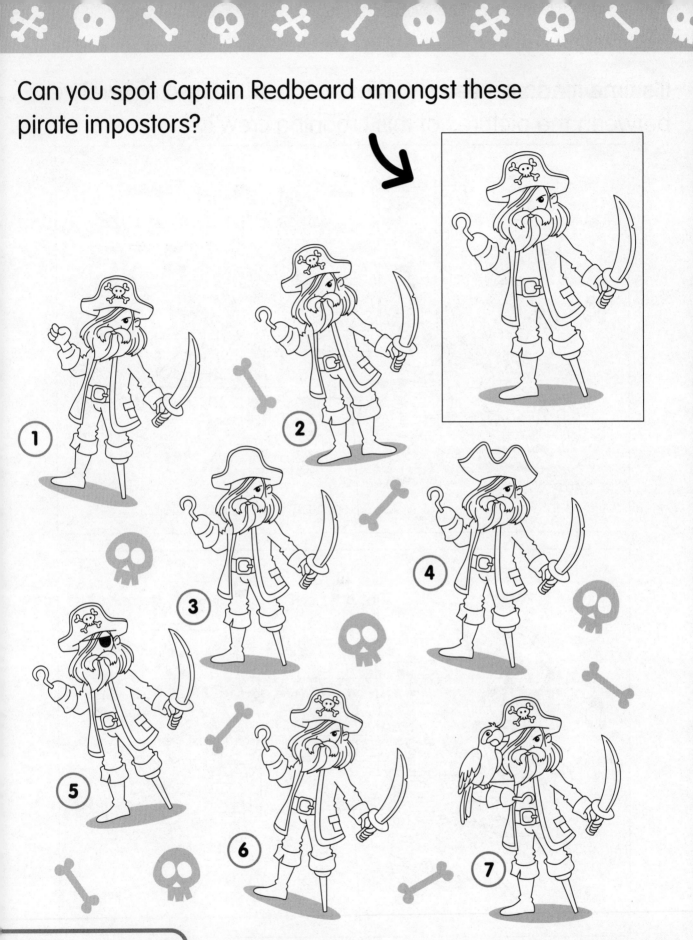

Can you find all these nautical words in the grid below?

Crow's nest
Booty
Deck
Sail
Mast
Plank

B	O	O	T	Y	E	F	E	N
L	E	I	I	E	F	C	O	O
C	R	O	W	S	N	E	S	T
N	B	D	N	D	M	R	N	N
O	P	R	K	C	U	I	P	M
I	S	C	A	S	A	I	L	M
Y	E	I	R	V	Y	U	A	A
D	P	B	K	I	D	S	N	S
C	R	S	A	I	A	T	K	T

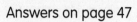

Answers on page 47

One of the crew has been looting treasure. Use the clues to find the culprit and make him walk the plank!

1. He's wearing stripes.
2. He does not have a beard.
3. He has an eye-patch.

Answer on page 47

This rough and tough captain is a softie at heart! Connect the dots to reveal his cuddly companion.

Answer on page 47

Which close-up from this pirate's spyglass doesn't appear in the picture?

a
b
c
d

Answer on page 47

Anchors away! How many anchors can you count?

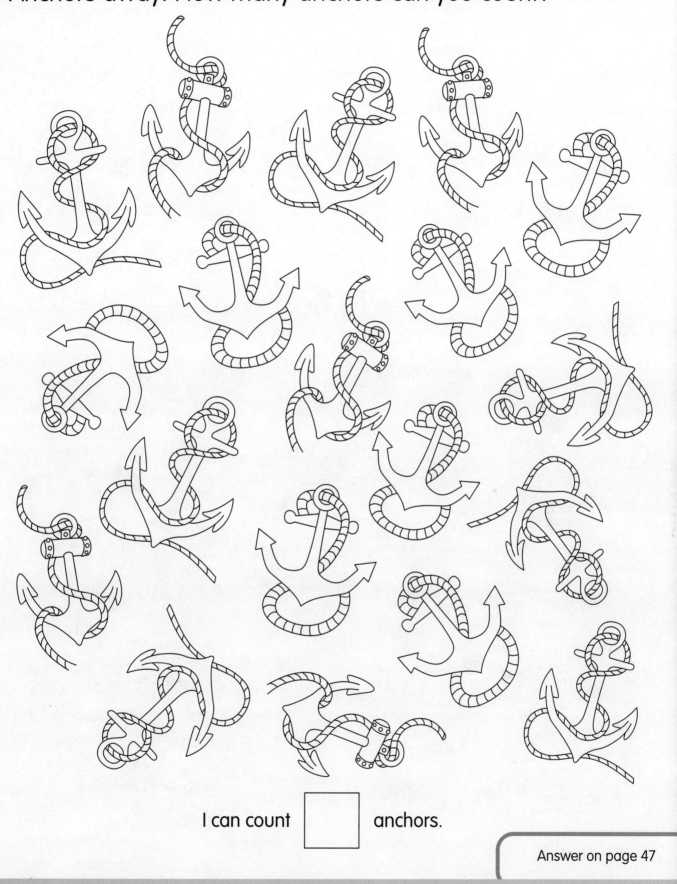

I can count ☐ anchors.

Answer on page 47

Can you match these slippery sea monsters into pairs?

Answers on page 47

Help the pirate climb up to the treasure by adding up the numbers under each square.

15

4   6

1   3   4   5   1

Answers on page 47

Pirates sail no matter the weather! Draw in the five missing things to make the pictures match.

Answers on page 47

This captain can't remember where he docked his ship!
Use the clues to help you find it.

1. It has three sails.
2. It has two portholes.
3. It doesn't have a skull sail.

Answer on page 47

It's a busy day at the docks! Answer these questions before the ships sail away.

1. Which ship is the biggest? . . . .

2. Which ship is the smallest? . . . .

3. Which ship has the most sails? . . . .

Answers on page 47

Which path will lead the pirate to the treasure?

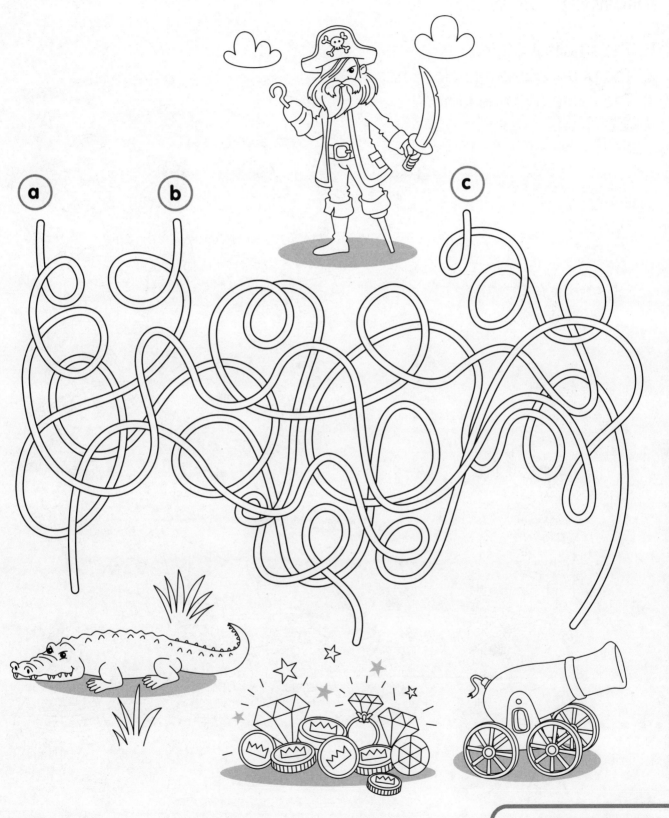

Answer on page 47

There are lots of pirates at this party. See if you can spot the following:

1. The smallest pirate.
2. The pirate with a hook for a hand.
3. The pirate with one tooth.

Answers on page 48

Which pirate is missing something from his treasure hoard?

Answer on page 48

Captain Cutlass is proud of his new portrait. Spot which painting is his by matching him to the picture.

Answer on page 48

Every crew member is important! Draw lines to connect each job to the correct pirate.

Chef   Cleaner   Navigator   Captain   Parrot tamer

1

2

3

4

5

Answers on page 48

This pirate needs your help breaking the code! Circle every other letter on the scroll to reveal the location of the treasure.

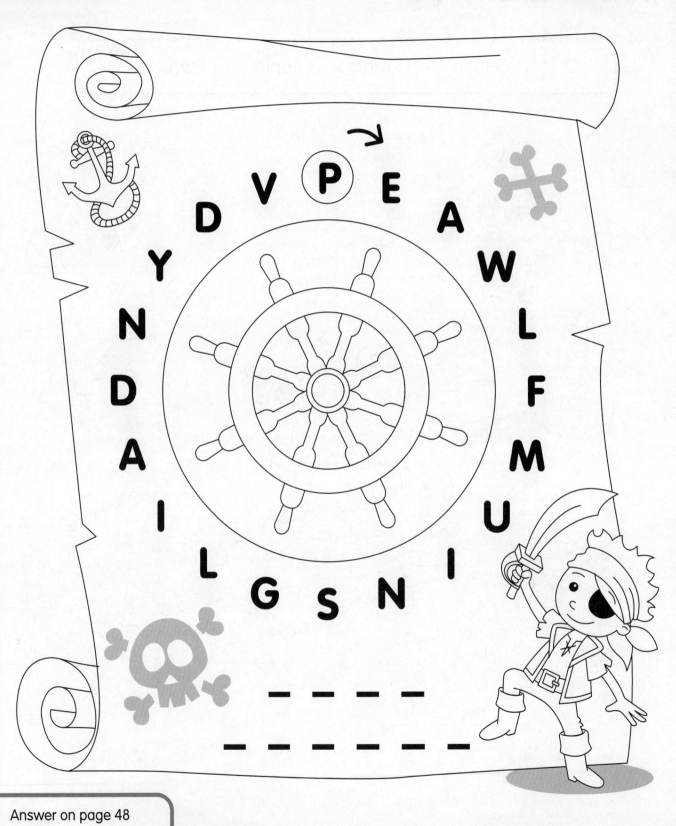

_ _ _ _ _
_ _ _ _ _

Answer on page 48

Match each close-up to a member of the crew.

Answers on page 48

Let's go on an adventure! Find a route across the sea.

Start

Croc Cave

Treasure Island

Palm Island   Mermaid Lagoon

Finish

What places did you go along the way?

_____ and _____

Answers on page 48

Answer Page

Page 2

Page 3

Page 4
1. 2 treasure chests
2. A skull and cross-bones
3. An octopus
4. 1 pirate hat

Page 5
There are 17 swords.

Page 6
1. 8
2. 8
3. 9
4. 12

Page 7
There are 6 cannon balls.

Page 8

Page 9

Page 10

Page 11

Page 12

Page 14

Page 15
Pirate 9.

Page 16
1b, 2c, 3a.

Page 17
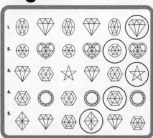

Page 18

Page 19

Answer Page

Page 20
She should join crew b.

Page 21

Page 22

Page 23

Page 24
1 crab, 2 shells, 6 coins, 3 rings and 2 bottles.

Page 25

Page 26
6 is Captain Redbeard.

Page 27

Page 28

Page 29

Page 30
Item c doesn't appear.

Page 31
There are 19 anchors.

Page 32

Page 33

Page 34

Page 35

Page 36
1. b
2. c
3. b

Page 37
Path c leads to the treasure.

Page 38

1.    2.

3.

Page 39

Pirate d is missing a jewel.

Page 40

The correct painting is d.

Page 41

1. Parrot tamer
2. Cleaner
3. Chef
4. Navigator
5. Captain

Page 42

The location is PALM ISLAND.

Page 43

1d, 2a, 3c, 4b.

Pages 44–45

You visited Croc Cave and Treasure Island on the way.